This
belongs to...
Elisha 9
Reeves

The
Flower Fairies

Illustrated by
Margaret W. Tarrant

Original poetry by
Marion St. John Webb

Series Editor

Fiona Waters

·MARGARET TARRANT'S·
FAIRIES & FLOWERS

First published in this format in 2002 by
The Medici Society Ltd
Grafton House, Hyde Estate Road, London NW9 6JZ

Copyright © The Medici Society Ltd 2002 / 1923

First published in 1923 by The Medici Society Ltd
3 5 7 9 10 8 6 4 2

The rights of Margaret Tarrant and Marion St John Webb to be identified
as the Illustrator and Author of this work have been asserted by them in
accordance with the Copyright, Design and Patents Act 1988.

A catalogue record for this book is available from the British Library.

ISBN 0 85503 258 8

Margaret Tarrant's original artworks have been rescanned for this re-designed edition.

Designed by Tony Potter Publishing Ltd

Printed in Singapore

The
Flower Fairies

Contents

The Magic Window

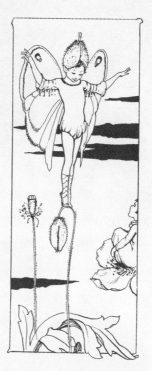

There are fairies in my garden,
    And I never guessed at all!
I used to weed the path
And train the ivy up the wall,
And take my yellow watering can
And water all the flowers.

I'd watch the little snails and things,
And hoe and dig for hours.
While all the time the fairies
Must have smiled and laughed at me,
And danced away from under my feet,
But I could never see.

There are fairies in my garden,
And I'll tell you how I know.
There is a little window
In the green house, hidden down below.
And yesterday I looked through it,
And then the fairies came!

I could see my garden,
But it didn't look the same.
Along the paths, and on the flowers,
And all about the grass,
Were fairies, and little elves too,
I saw them through the glass.

I know that magic window
Will let me see them all.
I look through, and there they are!
But if I make a noise or call
Or run outside to touch them,
Why then, they are not there at all!

The Magic Window

Pretending

If I look through my magic window
    There is so much to see.
The poppies in the garden
All nod their heads at me.

And when I look I sometimes see
A flash of shiny wings.
The Poppy Elves are there
They are such tiny things.

They climb right in the flowers,
And there begin to play,
And sometimes I can almost hear
Exactly what they say.

They play pretending games,
The way that I do too,
And pretend they're riding on a bus,
Or visiting the Zoo.

They play at schools,
They pretend they cannot fly.
And when the teacher gets too cross,
Then they pretend to cry.

A naughty elf pretended once
That she was just like me
As she ran around the garden,
For all the rest to see.

The others all laughed and laughed.
It was more than I could bear.
I couldn't even look at them,
It simply wasn't fair!

There are some times, of course,
When I pretend an elf to be.
I curl up small and close my eyes
But really all the time I'm me!

M. W. Tarrant.

The Flowers that
Frighten Me

Standing tall and stiff and still,
   Like soldiers in a row,
The red and purple tulips
In straight long lines do grow.

Very proud and grand they look.
I'm sure they've never played.
If I was a fairy small
Of them I'd be afraid.

But fairies do not seem to think
Of minding them a bit!
They shake the stalks, and climb up them,
And in the flowers sit.

They slide along the leaves,
Which must be very tough,
Those bad fairies pull them so.
Oh, they can be rough!

And then I'm frightened just in case
Those cross tulips might
Do something rather dreadful
To pay them back one night.

For the tulips talk at dusk
If the fairies are not there.
I listened once and heard them.
It gave me quite a scare!

And everyone was whispering,
Heads nodding up and down.
They looked as if they had real faces
And every face wore a frown.

And they planned such dreadful things,
And said they'd do them too!
I'm frightened for the fairies,
In case, one day, they do.

Tea with a Fairy

The Peaseblossom Fairy
Is quiet as a mouse.
She's pretty, and she's gentle,
And she lives in a little house.
It has a real door-bell
On a real front door.
And there's a real letter-box,
Now what can that be for?

For fairies never write letters at all,
It's much quicker, they say, to fly and call.

The Peaseblossom Fairy
Is as friendly as can be.
She's always asking other fairies
To come in for a cup of tea.
And specially the old ones,
And one that is a bore.
She asks them all, and in they come,
Still more and more, through the door.

And through her letter-box they shout,
To find out if she is in or out.

The Peaseblossom Fairy
Is pleasant to them all.
The bees, and wasps, and spiders,
She invites them all to call.
She doesn't mind how many,
Or if they've been before,
She asks them in, the lot of them,
And sits them round the floor.

And those she seems most glad to see
Are those who no-one else invites to tea.

Margaret W Tarrant

"Dragon's Mouth"

A naughty elf I often see
    Hiding behind the old willow tree.
He always has such games and fun
Teasing the fairies, one by one.

He will creep through the grass
And jump out on them as they pass.
Or he'll hide the things they need,
Which makes them very cross indeed.

All day long he's so quick
Full of mischief and sneaky tricks.
So all the other little elves
Have to watch out for themselves.

In and out, he'll play for hours,
Round about the trees and flowers.
He hides behind the snap-dragons tall,
That grow along the garden wall.

And the flowers he will squeeze,
To make a dragon's mouth, just to tease.
As elves and fairies walk on by
He tries so hard to make them cry.

But they just laugh and run away.
"We know who it is," they all say.
Then the naughty little elf
Has to play all by himself.

But when at night he goes to bed
Dragons fill his sleepy head,
And so his mother leaves a light
By his bedside, every night.

Singing in the Dark

From inside the blue larkspur
A little face is peeping.
Hush! Keep still!
And out he'll come creeping.
Right up to the very top
He will swiftly run.
  It's the Larkspur Fairy
  Laughing in the sun.

And when the wind is blowing
He will leap about,
And climb the flowers swaying
And smile and laugh and shout.
The wind blows his hat off
It ruffles up his hair.
  Here's the Larkspur Fairy
  Dancing on the air!

Outside in the garden
The rain comes pitter patter.
I hear a little voice
Whatever is the matter?
I peep out and what can I see
Looking through the window-pane?
  It is the Larkspur Fairy
  Crying in the rain.

And when I have to go to bed
I climb the stairs at night.
I snuggle down, warm and safe,
Beside my bedside light.
Then outside in the garden
In the moonlight bright
  I can hear the Larkspur Fairy
  Singing through the night.

Margaret Winifred Tarrant (1888 - 1959)

'Every time a child says, " I don't believe in fairies," ' warned Peter Pan, 'there is a little fairy somewhere that falls down dead.' By her paintings Margaret Tarrant did as much to encourage children's belief in fairies as J M Barrie did by his writings. Born in London in 1888, the only child of artist Percy Tarrant and his wife Sarah, Margaret excelled at art from an early age, and she was only 19 when she received her first, very prestigious, commission, from J M Dent & Sons: to illustrate Charles Kingsley's much-loved children's classic, *The Water Babies*, which was first published in 1863.

Her delicate, charming pictures matched the spirit of the story perfectly and earned her a string of new commissions: *Nursery Rhymes* (1914 and 1923), *Alice in Wonderland* (1916) and *Hans Andersen's Fairy Tales* (1917) for Ward Lock & Co., plus postcards for Oxford University Press.

Margaret Tarrant illustrated some 20 books for George G. Harrap & Co. between 1915 and 1929, but an even more important publishing relationship began in 1920, when she completed her first pieces for The Medici Society. This was to prove a long and fruitful connection, resulting in most of her best-known work. In the 1920s, for example, she illustrated this highly successful series of fairy books for the company, written by the poet and author Marion St John Webb. Her picture of Peter's Friends, inspired by J M Barrie's *Peter Pan* stories and the statue in Kensington Gardens, proved so popular when it appeared in 1921 that it had to be reproduced many times.

The dusk of the nineteenth and dawn of the twentieth centuries were magical times for fairy lovers. Fascination with fairy lore was widespread, reaching unprecedented heights in 1922 when Sir Arthur Conan Doyle

Peter's Friends

published *The Coming of the Fairies*, containing 'photographs' of fairies taken by two young girls in a Yorkshire village, which were later proved to be hoaxes. The story was actually a fascinating deception, which was believed by many reputable people. The mystery was not solved until towards the end of the twentieth century, when the girls involved, now elderly ladies, explained what had really happened.

In 1922, Margaret Tarrant's *Do You Believe in Fairies?* showed two children encircled by a ring of fairies, which caught the public excitement already created by Sir Arthur Conan Doyle's book. This interest was mirrored in an outpouring of art and literature. Children's books cultivated belief in fairies: they were used in religious teaching, magazines were devoted to them, and captivating new works appeared, most notably J M Barrie's *Peter Pan* and *Peter Pan in*

Do You Believe in Fairies?

Kensington Gardens. Rudyard Kipling wrote
Rewards and Fairies and even Beatrix Potter
embraced the subject in *The Fairy Caravan*.

Margaret Tarrant was one of those most associated
with the depiction of fairies in the 1920s and
1930s, together with her friend and sketching
partner, Cicely Mary Barker (1895 - 1973). Both
began to use Art Nouveau and Arts and Crafts
elements in their work, and in Tarrant's paintings
a breathtaking attention to detail - diaphanous
wings with the intricate tracery of a dragonfly's
wings - is a testament to the reality of fairies,
imaginary or otherwise.

During her life Margaret Tarrant tackled a wide
range of subjects and won special acclaim for
those, such as *All Things Wise and Wonderful*, with
a religious theme. But her forte was fairies, for in
her evocation of these ethereal figures she could
express her love for children, wild flowers and
dance, of all that was beautiful and pure.

Margaret Tarrant's fairies have a unique fluidity and balletic grace that expressed her delight in the free-flowing dance invented by Isadora Duncan. She was very much a free spirit herself, flying along the country lanes around her home in Surrey on an ancient bicycle, leaping off impulsively to sketch meticulously from life to capture the likeness of a child or plant. She never married, but she attracted many friends by her generosity, energy and zest for life. Perhaps it was this childlike enthusiasm and innocence, combined with a special kind of imagination, that gave her a natural affinity with fairies.

The Lily Pool

Much missed when she died in 1959, Margaret Tarrant left a lasting legacy in charming pictures that seem as fresh today as the day they were painted, and still enchant new generations with their glimpses into a secret fairy world.

The new edition

There are 12 beautiful fairy books by Margaret Tarrant,
originally published between 1923 - 1928. The
re-designed edition is now available to collect as a set,
with modern scanning methods used to bring out the
exquisite detail of the original paintings and drawings.

WATER FAIRIES — WATER FAIRIES

TWILIGHT FAIRIES — TWILIGHT FAIRIES

WEATHER FAIRIES — WEATHER FAIRIES

ORCHARD FAIRIES — ORCHARD FAIRIES

WILD FRUIT FAIRIES — WILD FRUIT FAIRIES

INSECT FAIRIES — INSECT FAIRIES

HOUSE FAIRIES — HOUSE FAIRIES

FOREST FAIRIES — FOREST FAIRIES

SEED FAIRIES — SEED FAIRIES

SEASHORE FAIRIES — SEASHORE FAIRIES

FLOWER FAIRIES — FLOWER FAIRIES

HEATH FAIRIES — HEATH FAIRIES